come away with me

Norah Jones

Exclusive distributors:
Music Sales Limited
8/9 Frith Street, London W1D 3JB, England.
Music Sales Pty Limited
120 Rothschild Avenue, Rosebery, NSW 2018, Australia.

Order No. AM975678
ISBN 0-7119-9694-6
This book © Copyright 2002 by Wise Publications.

Music arrangements by Jack Long.
Music processed by Paul Ewers Music Design.

Photographer Clive Arrowsmith.
Photograph courtesy of Camera Press.

Printed in the United Kingdom by
Caligraving Limited, Thetford, Norfolk.

www.musicsales.com

Your Guarantee of Quality:

As publishers, we strive to produce every book
to the highest commercial standards.

While endeavouring to retain the original running
order of the recorded album, the book has been
carefully designed to minimise awkward page turns
and to make playing from it a real pleasure.

Particular care has been given to specifying
acid-free, neutral-sized paper made from pulps which
have not been elemental chlorine bleached.

This pulp is from farmed sustainable forests and
was produced with special regard for the environment.

Throughout, the printing and binding have been
planned to ensure a sturdy, attractive publication
which should give years of enjoyment.

If your copy fails to meet our high standards,
please inform us and we will gladly replace it.

Wise Publications
London/New York/Paris/Sydney/Copenhagen/Berlin/Madrid/Tokyo

Don't Know Why

Words & Music by Jesse Harris

4

Verse 3:
Out across the endless sea
I will die in ecstasy
But I'll be a bag of bones
Driving down the road alone.

My heart is drenched in wine etc.

Verse 4:
Something has to make you run
I don't know why I didn't come
I feel as empty as a drum
I don't know why I didn't come
I don't know why I didn't come
I don't know why I didn't come

5

Seven Years

Words & Music by Lee Alexander

1. Spin - ning,_ laugh - ing, danc - ing to her fav - 'rite song,_
(Verse 4 instrumental)

*Fra - gile as___ a leaf___ in Au -
- tumn just fall - in' to the ground___ with -
- out a sound.___ 3. Crook - ed___ lit - tle smile___
(Verse 6 see block lyric)
___ on___ her face___ tells___

Verse 6:
Spinning, laughing, dancing to her favourite song
She's a little girl with nothing wrong
And she's all alone.

Cold Cold Heart

Words & Music by Hank Williams

melt your cold,__ cold heart?_____

2. An -__ heart?_

heart? _____ heart. _____ Hey, hey, hey, _____ hey, _____ hey.

(8vb)

_____ Ah ha. _____

Verse 2:
Another love before my time
Made your heart sad and blue,
And so my heart is paying now
For things I didn't do.
In anger, unkind words I say
That make the teardrops start,
Why can't I free your doubtful mind
And melt your cold, cold heart?

Verse 3:
There was a time when I believed
That you belong to me,
But now I know your heart is shackled
To a memory.
The more I learn to care for you
The more we drift apart,
Why can't I free your doubtful mind
And melt your cold, cold heart?

Feelin' The Same Way

Words & Music by Lee Alexander

1. The sun just slipped its note___ be-
(Verses 2 & 3 see block lyrics)

low my___ door,___ and I can't hide be-neath___ my___

singin' the same lines all over again, no

matter how much I pretend.

(Ad lib. Vocal)

Ah._____

rit.

Verse 2:
Another day that I can't find my head
My feet don't look like they're my own
I'll try and find the floor below to stand
And I hope I reach it once again.

And I'm feelin' the same way *etc.*

Verse 3:
So many times I wonder where I've gone
And how I found my way back in
I look around a while for something lost
Maybe I'll find it in the end.

And I'm feelin' the same way *etc.*

Come Away With Me

Words & Music by Norah Jones

1. Come a-way with me in the night.___
(Verses 2, 5 & 6 see block lyrics)

stop lov - ing you.

you to come a - way with me in the night.

Come a - way with me.

Verse 2:
Come away with me on a bus
Come away where they can't tempt us
With their lies.

Verses 5 & 6:
Instrumental

Verse 7:
And I want to wake up with the rain
Falling on a tin roof
While I'm safe there in your arms
So all I ask is for you
To come away with me in the night
Come away with me.

Turn Me On

Words & Music by John D. Loudermilk

Lonestar

Words & Music by Lee Alexander

Verse 2:
How far you are I just don't know
The distance I'm willing to go
I pick up a stone that I cast to the sky
Hoping for some kind of sign.

Verse 3:
Instrumental

I've Got To See You Again

Words & Music by Jesse Harris

1. Lines_____ on your face_____ don't both -
(Verses 2-5. see block lyrics)

down___ in___ my___ chair___

when you dance___ ov - er me.___ I can't help___

To Coda ⊕

___ my - self, I've got to see___ you___ a-

1. Fm

-gain.

2, 4. Fm

-gain.

Verse 2:
Late in the night when I'm all alone
And I look at the clock and I know you're not home
I can't help myself
I've got to see you again.

Verse 3:
But no, I won't go for any of those things
To not touch your skin is not why I sing
I can't help myself
I've got to see you again.

Verse 4:
Instrumental

Verse 5:
No I won't go to share you with them
But oh even though I know where you've been
I can't help myself
I've got to see you again.

Shoot The Moon

Words & Music by Jesse Harris

1. The sum - mer days_____ are gone_____
(Verses 2 see block lyrics, verse 3 instr. til *)

— too soon; you shoot the moon and miss com - plete - ly._____

Verse 2:
Now the fall is here again
You can't begin to give in, its all over
When the snows come rolling through
You're rolling too with some new lover
Will you think of times you've told me
That you knew the reason
Why we had to each be lonely?
It was just the season.

Verse 3:
(Instrumental)
Will you think of times you've told me
That you knew the reason
Why we had to each be lonely?
It was just the season.

Painter Song

Words & Music by Lee Alexander & J.C. Hopkins

1. If I were a pain - ter,___ I would paint my re - ver-

-ge - ther___ just___ like we___ used to

(Verse 3 instrumental till *)

One Flight Down

Words & Music by Jesse Harris

1. One flight down, there's a song on

low, and your mind_____ just picked up___ on___ the sound.

_____ Now you know_____ that you're_____ wrong, be - cause it

drifts_____ like_____ smoke, and it's been

_____ there play - ing all___ a - long._____ Now you know,

now____ you know.____

2. The reeds__ and brass have__ been____ weav - ing,____
(Verse 3 see block lyric)

lead - ing in - to__ a sin - gle note._____

In_____ this__ place, where your arms__ un -

Verse 3:
The cadence rolls in broken
Plays it over and then goes
One flight down
There's a song on low
And it's been there playing all along
Now you know
Now you know.

Nightingale

Words & Music by Norah Jones

The Nearness Of You

Words by Ned Washington
Music by Hoagy Carmichael .

The Long Day Is Over

Words & Music by Norah Jones & Jesse Harris

12/02 (46191)